GW00672183

Task Sheet 6

Name ....   *Date* ....

Name ....

Date ....

Task Sheet 6

Year 5 Life Cycles

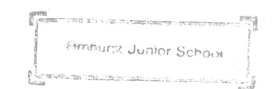

Life Cycles

Contents

About this unit

In this unit children's ideas about how plants and animals reproduce are further developed. This unit is best taught when there are plants in flower, or in autumn when plants can be seen bearing fruit.

The unit builds on work developed in 'Health and Growth', 'Helping Plants Grow' and 'Keeping Healthy'. Children learn that fruits and seeds are made by flowers. They also learn that the flower is the structure that contains the male and female reproductive cells that are brought together to make the seeds. The children examine fruits and explore the different mechanisms plants use for seed dispersal. They also investigate the conditions necessary for seeds to germinate. Children learn about stages in their own life cycle and the importance of reproduction to the survival of the species.

Scientific enquiry is planned into the unit and focuses on:
- planning a fair test investigation.
- considering and drawing conclusions from evidence.
- drawing line graphs and bar charts to present data.

Background Scientific Information

Life cycles

This unit considers the life cycles of flowering plants and animals. The life cycle is concerned with the life process of reproduction and growth for maintaining the species. A species is an organism that can reproduce with its own kind to give young that are fertile – that is, it can reproduce, when ready, to keep the life cycle going. It is possible to mate some species of animals and plants with different species so they have infertile young or seeds. When a male donkey and a female horse are mated, a mule is produced. However, a mule can not produce a mule by being mated with another mule.

Reproduction in flowering plants

Flowering plants reproduce by making seeds in their flowers. Seeds are produced when pollen from a male flower reaches the female parts of a flower and fertilisation takes place.

Most plants have flowers with both male and female reproductive parts. These **hermaphrodite** or **bisexual** plants may pollinate themselves (self-pollination) but they are more often pollinated by another plant (cross-pollination). Some plants have separate male and female flowers. In **monoecious** plants such as roses, the male and female flowers are on the same plant. On a **dioecious** plant such as holly, the flowers are either all male or all female. Pollen from a male holly tree must reach flowers on a female holly tree for fertilisation to happen. Children should study plant reproduction using flowers with both male and female parts.

Part of flower	Special features	Job/purpose
Sepals	Green leaves collectively called the calyx.	Protects flower before it opens. Leaves a scar on the fruit when removed from it, for example, the small green button of leaves on an orange or strawberry.
Stamen	Consists of slender filament and anther.	Male part of flower which makes pollen. Pollen is the male reproductive cell. Pollination is the transfer of pollen from stamen to stigma. It can be done by insects or the wind, or by humans when engaged in selective breeding programmes.

Part of flower	Special features	Job/purpose
Carpel or pistil	Consists of stigma, style and ovary.	Female part of flower. The ovary has female reproductive cells. When the male reproductive cell joins with the female egg cell to fertilise it, the ovary swells to form a fruit that protects the seed. For a fruit to form naturally, the egg must be fertilised. However, it is possible to spray flowers with plant hormones to make fruit formation happen without fertilisation. This is how seedless grapes are made. Fruits have two scars: the remains of the stigma that looks like a pin at one end, and the remains of the sepals at the opposite end of the fruit.
Petals	Often coloured and perfumed with honey guides that lead to a sweet smelling nectar gland.	Attract insects that seek pollen to flowers. As they enter the flower, they can transfer pollen collected from another flower to the stigma where it sticks to a sugary liquid that also helps the pollen grain to travel and germinate down the style to the ovary. Pollination is an essential prerequisite to fertilisation.

Seed dispersal

Fruits and seeds need to be dispersed to maintain the plant life cycle, and plants have different mechanisms for dispersing their seeds.

Dispersal mechanism	Example
Wind	Dandelion, ash, thistle, poppy, grass.
Water	Coconut.
Explosion	Himalayan balsam, lupin, peas and beans, horse chestnut.
Animal	Tomato, blackberry, raspberry, plum, apple, acorns, hazelnuts, burdock, goose grass.

More fruits and seeds are produced than will ever develop into plants – this is an insurance mechanism for maintaining continuity of the species. Also, many seeds provide food for animals which, in turn, transport seeds to new habitats.

Germination

This is the process by which a flowering plant starts to grow from a seed – it is the start of growth. The seed has a built-in supply of food. When conditions are right for germination, the food is used for cell respiration (the process by which oxygen and sugar are used in the cells to produce energy, carbon dioxide and water) and as raw material for making new plant cells. Gradually, the plant embryo develops into a small plant with small roots, a stem and its first leaves. A seed needs water and warmth, and must be correctly physically developed, before it can germinate. After germination the plant will need light to photosynthesise and make food, but light is not needed by most seeds in order to start germinating. Some seeds need fire to start germinating and others won't germinate until they've passed through an animal's gut.

There are two types of germination: **epigeal** and **hypogeal**. With hypogeal germination the seed remains below the ground; for example, broad beans and peas. With epigeal germination the seed coat is raised above the ground; for example, spring onions and sunflowers. This knowledge is useful for selecting different seeds to germinate in the classroom so that their similarities and differences can be observed.

Animal life cycles

Animals must reproduce for the species to survive. Mammals reproduce by sexual means. This involves two reproductive cells or **gametes** joining together at fertilisation. In mammals, fertilisation is internal and the egg develops into an embryo within the female body. The length of time it takes for an embryo to develop in the female uterus is termed the gestation period. The gestation period varies for different species but, as a general rule, the larger the mammal the longer the gestation period. For example, the gestation period of a mouse is 21 days and that of an elephant is 624 days.

The human life cycle is long and children need parental or suitable adult care to reach social, sexual and emotional maturity to be able, in turn, to provide years of care for rearing a child. The effective biological function of an animal is complete when it has reproduced and reared young to reproductive age. If the birth rate of an animal population is less than the death rate then that population is not replacing itself. It becomes an endangered species and could face extinction. Breeding animals in captivity to release into their natural environment is one way of supporting an endangered species. Protecting their habitat is another.

Scheme of Work:

Learning objective: Knowledge and understanding	Task	Learning objective: Skills	Literacy and numeracy links	Resources and safety	Evidence of learning Children:
Flowering plants reproduce.	**1 What are your ideas about seeds and fruit?** Children offer their ideas about the origin of seeds. **2 Where do seeds come from?** Children look at pictures of seeds from different plants and trace them back to the flower. **3 Go on a fruit hunt.** Children study a selection of fruits and look for their seeds. They make observational drawings of fruits and seeds, including a citrus fruit. They compare a variety of citrus fruits.	Plan, obtain and consider evidence from seeds found in a variety of fruits.	Data handling. Note-making .	**Task Sheet 1.** Pictures of fruits and their flowers. Fruits from different plants (e.g. daffodils or nasturtiums), citrus fruits, knives, cutting boards, fruit squeezer, observational aids. CD-ROMs, Internet access. **Safety!** Children should not taste any seeds and fruits provided. Avoid using nuts, especially peanuts, as some children are allergic to these. Cut any fruit yourself, or supervise the children closely.	Can draw and write to show their ideas about how flowering plants reproduce. Can recognise that seeds are found in or on fruits. Can recognise that fruits develop from flowers.
Seeds provide food for humans and other animals. Seeds are dispersed in different ways.	**4 Talking seeds.** Children match speech bubbles from seeds talking about their method of seed dispersal to different seeds. **5 Poppy population.** Children answer questions about the dispersal of four varieties of poppies.	Consider evidence and relate patterns in results to scientific knowledge.	Note-making. Data handling, interpreting data in tables.	**Task Sheet 2.** CD-ROMs, Internet access.	Can describe how seeds can be dispersed by water, wind, explosion and animals, giving examples of each. Can interpret data in tables and explain that the number of seeds produced can be a measure success.
Seeds need the right conditions to germinate. Plan and carry out a fair test.	**6 What do seeds need to germinate?** Children raise questions about what seeds need to germinate and, with support, plan a fair test, collect evidence and interpret it.	Plan a fair test. Obtain and present evidence. Consider and evaluate evidence.	Data handling. Organising and interpreting data. Speaking and listening.	**Task Sheet 3.** Some seeds (e.g. cress, radish, spring onion, lettuce, peas, beans.), kitchen paper, compost and soil, seed trays or other suitable containers, labels, water, a measuring cylinder or beaker.	Can plan and carry out a fair test into conditions for germination. Can record using a table.
Plants produce flowers, fruits and seeds.	**7 A closer look at a flower.** Children discuss the parts of a flower using text and diagrams.		Directed activity related to text (DART). Locate and retrieve information confidently and efficiently.		Can name the parts of the flower, e.g. stamen, petal, style and sepal, and explain their functions. Can complete a table.
	8 Taking flowers apart. **9 Flower identification cards.** Children take apart different flowers and mount them on card. They identify the parts of the flower for each example and make an ID card for a flower.			**Task Sheets 4,5.** Different flowers. Tweezers. Database software.	Can make a flower identification card and name the different parts of the flower.
Flowers need pollinating to make fruit and seeds.	**10 Pollination. 11 Insect pollination.** Children explain pollination. They use pictures of pollen to discuss adaptations for wind and insect pollination, possibly carrying out a microscopic observation of pollen. They observe insects pollinating plants and write a poem or story for other children to read.	Obtain evidence and record it in a table.	Literacy: writing non-fictional text. Writing a poem.	Monocular microscope and slide, flower pollen, reference books and pictures of pollen and pollination. **Safety!** Children may have allergies to pollen.	Can explain that pollination is the transfer of pollen from stamen to stigma. Can observe pollen and identify some distinctive features. Can observe insects pollinating flowers.

Learning objective: Knowledge and understanding	Task	Learning objective: Skills	Literacy and numeracy links	Resources and safety	Evidence of learning Children:
Insects pollinate some flowers.	**12 Pollination Street.** Children devise a cartoon strip to explain how pollen from one plant reaches the stigma of another plant of the same species.		Read and write instructional text.	**Task Sheet 6.**	Can explain that pollen is transferred from stamen to stigma in pollination.
	13 Fast plants. Children use information from a table to plot and interpret a graph about the growth of 'fast plants'.	Make a line graph with support. Describe patterns on the line graph. Use results to make predictions.	Handling data. Drawing a line graph and interpreting it. Using a computer to prepare a spreadsheet and graphs.	**Task Sheet 7.** Spreadsheets and graphing software.	Can draw a line graph and interpret evidence. Can identify the stages of the life cycle of a plant.
Animals have a life cycle of birth, growth, reproduction and death.	**14 Spot the life cycle.** Children use pictures to identify the key stages of a life cycle. **15 Growing up.** Children write their ideas on changing height and weight with age. **16 Keeping the life cycle going.** Children study the life cycle process.		Literacy: writing non-fictional text.	**Task Sheet 8.** Word processor.	Can explain the stages of development from baby to later junior years.
	17 Family trees. Children interpret a family tree and recognise the importance of adults needing to reproduce to keep the life cycle going.	Consider evidence and seek patterns.		Drawing software.	Can interpret a family tree. Know how to create a family tree. Can explain that adults have young and these grow into adults and also produce young.
If living things don't reproduce they die out.	**18 Life spans.** Children examine the life spans of some animals, reorder the data and make a bar graph.	Consider evidence and relate patterns in results to scientific knowledge. Order results, make bar graphs and seek patterns.	Numeracy: handling data, interpreting data in tables and graphs.	Spreadsheets and graphing software.	Can read and interpret data in a table. Can explain that animal life spans vary. Can reorder data and produce a bar graph.
	19 Survival Game. Children play a game which involves thinking about disasters and success for the human species.			**Task Sheet 9.** Counters, dice and shakers.	Can describe some factors that can harm the life cycle. Can recognise that for the human species to survive some individuals must reproduce.
	Checkpoint. Children research endangered species.			CD-ROMs, reference books, the Internet. Word processor or DTP software.	
	Summary. Children read through the statements and complete the **Science Log**.			**Science Log.**	
	Assessment Tasks. Children do structured tests to assess their knowledge, skills and understanding of life cycles.			**Assessment Task Sheets A and B.**	

Information and Communication Technology

Where appropriate, ideas for ICT opportunities are included throughout the Teacher's Notes. The table below indicates where ICT skills could be developed in this unit.

Task	ICT Opportunity
2 Where do seeds come from?	*Research using CD-ROMs and the Internet.*
5 Poppy population	*Research using CD-ROMs and the Internet.*
9 Flower identification cards	*Use database software to make flower identification cards and record the details of the flower.*
13 Fast plants	*Use spreadsheets and graphing software to display results as a line graph.*
16 Keeping the life cycle going	*Word process a sequence of pages to show the human life cycle.*
17 Family trees	*Use DTP or drawing software to draw family trees.*
18 Life spans	*Use spreadsheets and graphing software.*
Checkpoint	*Research endangered species using CD-ROMs, Internet and reference books. Word process a poster or leaflet or use DTP.*

What are your ideas about seeds and fruit?

TASK 1

Purpose

For children to express their ideas about where seeds and fruit come from.

What to do

Use this activity, together with **Task Sheet 1**, to find out the children's initial ideas. Encourage the children to work independently and limit discussion until later. Explain that you are interested in their ideas rather than the 'right' answers. Set a time limit, e.g. 15 minutes. Collect their responses.

Where do seeds come from?

TASK 2

Purpose

For children to know that flowering plants make seeds to reproduce, and that seeds originally come from the flowers on flowering plants.

What to do

Look at the sequences of pictures in the book. The children should notice that in each example the seed came originally from the flower. Ask them to find three more examples of seeds and the flowers that they came from.

QUESTIONS

o Where did the seed come from?

Possible answers

A flower or fruit.

ICT OPPORTUNITY

Children could use CD-ROMs and the Internet for their research.

Watch out for!

Safety! Children should not taste any seeds and fruits provided. Avoid using nuts, especially peanuts, as some children are allergic to these.

Go on a fruit hunt

TASK 3

Purpose

For children to observe carefully some fruits and seeds, and to know that fruits are found on a variety of flowering plants and that they contain seeds.

What to do

Provide the children with a range of 'safe' fruits, but instruct them not to taste them (unless you specifically want to develop the activity further). Alternatively, you might hunt for fruits in the school grounds or local park. Remind them to look for newly-formed fruits where flowers used to be. They could bring one or two examples back the classroom, but stress that plants are living things and that we must take care of them.

Children observe and draw their fruits and a seed for each fruit. If you use citrus fruits, cut them in half and ask the children to try squeezing them to separate the seeds. Remind them that the part we eat and the seeds have all developed from the flower. You might set homework for the children to survey the number of seeds in fruits such as lemons and oranges, with the children working closely with an adult. In a later lesson consider how many seeds were counted by the children and why plants make large numbers of seeds.

Use the **Fact File** on baked beans on page 4 to highlight that seeds are important sources of human food.

QUESTIONS

- Name some things that scientists would call fruits that people in everyday life would not.
- Where would you look for fruits on plants outside?
- When you get back in the classroom, how will you be able to check that you have got a fruit?

Possible answers

Tomatoes, peas in a pod, conkers in their shells, a lupin pod, a poppy head, etc.
Where the flowers used to be.

Look for seeds forming inside.

Watch out for!

Safety! Avoid using unsafe fruits and seeds – the lupin is poisonous. Check these with the ASE book Be Safe! Cut any fruit yourself, or supervise the children closely if they cut it themselves. Some fruits, such as strawberries, have their seeds on the outside. Be aware that some oranges have been specifically grown to be seedless

Talking seeds

TASK 4

Purpose

For children to know that seeds can be dispersed in a variety of ways, including animals, water, explosion and wind.

What to do

Discuss seed dispersal with the children and let them read the **Fact File**. Bring out reasons why it helps a newly-formed plant to grow further away from the parent plant. Encourage the children to look closely at the pictures and to try to match each speech bubble to the correct seed or fruit. Point out that there are two examples of seed dispersal by wind, two of dispersal by animal and only one of explosion and water. Children can use **Task Sheet 2** to extend their understanding.

QUESTIONS

- Almost all plants have developed ways of making sure that their seeds germinate and grow away from the parent plant. Why do you think this has happened?

Possible answers

If the seeds tried to grow close to the parent plant they would have to compete for light and water (and nutrients).

Poppy population

TASK 5

Purpose

For children to consider the dispersal of poppy seeds and draw conclusions about the relationship between number of seeds produced and the frequency of the plants' appearance.

What to do

Make sure that the children realise how the poppy seeds come out of the capsule. If possible, bring some poppy heads into school so that they can see and handle the capsules. Allow the children to complete the activity before discussing their answers.

The Extra Challenge provides an opportunity to research the connection between poppies and the First World War.

QUESTIONS	Possible answers
○ Which is the commonest poppy? Why?	*The field poppy probably because it makes more seeds per flower than the other types.*
○ Which is the rarest? Why?	*The long rough-headed poppy probably because it makes the fewest seeds per flower.*

ICT OPPORTUNITY

Children could use the Internet and CD-ROMs for research.

What do seeds need to germinate?

TASK 6

Purpose

For children to investigate the conditions needed for seeds to germinate by planning a fair test, obtaining and presenting evidence, and considering and evaluating the evidence collected.

What to do

The **Pupil's Book** shows some ideas that a group of children had about what seeds need to germinate. Encourage the children to discuss these ideas in groups and then as a whole class. List the range of ideas suggested on the board as 'wet/dry', 'wet warm/wet cold', 'dark/light' and 'soil/compost'. Then change the wording of the children's suggestions so that ideas are in a question format to enable an investigation to be planned and carried out. Allocate different investigations to different groups, ensuring that all the tests are covered, before holding a conference at the end to share the different results.

Discuss some of the points that are in the **Pupil's Book** and read the **Fact File** on page 8. Children should know that germination is a process of a seed beginning to grow. They will not measure growth of the plant but the number of days it takes for the radicle to appear. Encourage the use of several seeds for each part of the test to get reliable evidence.
Task Sheet 3 provides a planning board and table. This already gives the factor to measure (the dependent variable) so children have to make some decisions about only one heading (independent variable) for the table. Assessment could, therefore, focus on presenting and considering evidence in an appropriate way. Children should also draw a bar chart of class results.

QUESTIONS

Possible answers

- How many seeds will you use: lots or just a small spoonful?
- How much water will you use and how you will measure it?

Measuring cylinder or syringe.

- Where will you keep the germinating seeds and when will you check them?

Depends on the investigation, e.g. one in the light, one the dark; one in a warm place, one in a cold place, etc.

- When will you know that they have germinated?

When the radicle appears.

Then, after the investigation, ask:

- How do your findings relate to the time of year when most seeds are germinated in this country?

Seeds should grow most quickly in warm, moist conditions.

- Why is spring the time when most seeds germinate?

Spring often provides these conditions, and once the leaves have appeared, then more light is available to make food.

- Would autumn be a good time for seeds to germinate? Why?

Many new shoots could be killed by frost; it is colder so the growth would be slower – therefore, autumn is not a good time for germination.

The **Fact File** on page 9 discusses the fact that germination in hot deserts is dependent on rain to stimulate germination of seeds. Point out that these plants need to flower and make seeds quickly because it may be another 20 years before there is enough rain to stimulate germination.

 Watch out for!

Wash hands after handling seeds and soils; some may be treated with fungicide or pesticide. Use seeds that germinate quickly, such as radish, cress, mustard or spring onions. (Seeds do not need to develop into adult plants in this investigation.)

 TASK 7

A closer look at a flower

Purpose

For children to know that plants produce flowers and that these flowers have different parts which are adapted to carry out different functions.

What to do

Use the text to explain and discuss the main parts of the flower. Ask the children to retrieve information from the text and to complete the table.

Part of flower	Special features	Job/purpose
Sepals	Green leaves.	Protects flower before it opens
Stamen	*Made of slender filament and anther.*	*Male part of flower that makes pollen.*
Carpel or pistil	*Made of stigma, style and ovary.*	Female part of flower that makes seeds.
Petals	Often coloured and scented.	*Attract insects to flower to get pollen.*

 Watch out for!

Avoid using dandelions or daisies, which have composite flower heads, for teaching the flower structure. Instead, use buttercups, mallow or other, simpler flowers with male and female parts.

Taking flowers apart
Flower identification cards

TASK 8-9

Purpose

For children to be able to identify the different parts of a flower on several different specimens.

What to do

Provide the children with several different flowers. Try to make sure that they are flowers with only a few stamens (up to ten) and one carpel. It can be worth going to a florist if suitable flowers are not readily available. Make sure that the children pull the flower apart carefully on white paper so that they do not lose any parts of the flower. Compare all the different flowers at the end of the session. **Task Sheet 4** provides an opportunity for the children to draw and label two flowers.

Asking children to make an ID card for their flower reinforces the idea that plants have similar parts but that each flower, even those from the same species, has differences. It also encourages them to make careful observations and to take measurements. **Task Sheet 5** provides a template for the children to complete, although some children could make their own.

The ID cards can be displayed along with questions suggested by the children such as: Which flower has the longest stamens? How many flowers have more than four stamens? Which flower has the shortest carpel?

ICT OPPORTUNITY

Children could use database software to make flower identification cards and record the details of the flower.

Watch out for!

Flowers from plants such as daisies and dandelions have too many parts for children to handle easily and are best avoided at this stage. Some children may have allergies to pollen.

Pollination
Insect pollination

TASK
10-11

Purpose

For children to know that pollination is the transfer of pollen from the stamen to the stigma and that most plants make pollen that has special features. Insects are important for pollinating flowers.

What to do

Discuss and explain what pollination is and explain that plants make pollen that has special features. The **Pupil's Book** has photographs of pollen from some plants as seen under a microscope. Wind-borne pollen has wings and is light, small and relatively smooth. Insect-borne pollen is larger, heavier and sculptured with spines that can stick to insects' bodies. Ask the children to observe the different pollen grains and list the differences they notice. If you have a monocular microscope, put some pollen on a slide for the children to observe and draw.

For Task 11, visit a flowerbed and let the children quietly observe insects visiting the flowers. Use questions to direct their attention to the colour, shape and smell of the most frequently visited flowers over a 10 minute period. They could write a story or a poem explaining to other children what they observed.

QUESTIONS

- What is the pollen like?
- Do you think this pollen is transferred by wind or insects? Why?
- Which flowers are visited most by insects?

Watch out for!

Safety! Do not use pollen from plants that may cause allergic responses. Check these in the ASE book *Be Safe!* Some children may be hay fever sufferers and an alternative activity could be offered, for example, viewing high resolution photographs of different pollens.

Pollination Street

TASK
12

Purpose

For children to know about the transfer of pollen from stamen or anther to stigma during pollination and that many plants cross-pollinate.

What to do

Before you start this activity, make sure that the children can identify the pollen on their flower cards and that they know that the stigma at the end of the carpel has no pollen. Show them the start of the cartoon strip and point out that some pollen is transferred by insects. Ask them to complete the cartoon on **Task Sheet 6**. In this case the plant is a cherry blossom which, like most plants, requires cross-pollination for fertilisation. The cartoon should continue to show: the insect landing on the flower and collecting pollen from the stamen on it's body; the insect flying over the road to the other tree; the insect landing on a flower stigma on the other tree, thus transferring pollen.

QUESTIONS

- Where does the flower make pollen?
- What does it look like?
- Where must the pollen get to when the flower is pollinated?
- How does the pollen stay on the stigma?

- Can most plants pollinate their own flowers?

- What is cross-pollination?

Possible answers

On the ends of the stamens on parts called anthers.

It's normally a fine, yellowish powder.

The pollen must reach the end of the carpel, called the stigma.

The end of the stigma is slightly sticky and catches the pollen.

No, most plants cannot pollinate their own flowers. They have to cross-pollinate.

The pollen from one flower must land on the stigma of a flower of another plant of the same species.

TASK 13

Fast plants

Purpose

For children to know that flowering plants have a life cycle that includes pollination, fertilisation, seed production, seed dispersal and germination. For them to know that the life cycle goes from seed to seed and to use secondary evidence to plot a line graph and interpret it.

What to do

Make sure that the children can put together all the separate processes that they have learned about to form a life cycle, that is: a plant grows flowers, flowers are pollinated, the ovules are fertilised, the fruits grow, seeds form in the fruits, the seeds disperse, some of the seeds germinate, they grow into plants, the plants grow flowers, etc. Tell them that they will be asked to find out some information about a special 'fast plant' (brassica) which completes its life cycle from seed to seed in about 30 days. The plant is similar to oil seed rape, which they may know. **Task Sheet 7** provides a graph template to help them plot a line graph. Check that the graphs are correctly drawn before the children try to answer the questions.

QUESTIONS

- When was the plant 8 cm high?
- What height would you expect the plant to be on day 14?
- Between which two readings did the plant grow fastest?
- At the end, the line on your graph is flat. Why is this?

Possible answers

On day 11.

Around 12 cm.

Day 11 to day 15.

The plant has stopped growing.

ICT OPPORTUNITY

Children could use spreadsheets and graphing software to display their results as a line graph.

Watch out for!

Make sure that the children realise that the time intervals in the table are not evenly spaced.

Spot the life cycle

TASK 14

Purpose

For children to know that adults have young and that these grow into adults that also have young. For them to know also that an animal life cycle has stages of birth, growth, reproduction and death.

What to do

The **Pupil's Book** shows some photographs of different life cycle stages. The photographs show birth, growth, reproduction and death, which can be discussed with the children. **Task Sheet 8** shows pictures of stages in the life cycle of a bird, which are in the wrong order. The children should discuss the life cycle of the bird and mark on the stages. Children show their understanding by reordering them correctly.

QUESTIONS

○ What do animals' life cycles have in common?

Possible answers

They all have birth, growth, reproduction and death.

Watch out for!

This work is likely to support the school's programme for personal, social and health education and should be consistent with the school's sex education policy.

Growing up

TASK 15

Purpose

For children to know that human young are dependent on adults and for them to analyse their own growth and development.

What to do

In this activity, children write their ideas about their own development from a baby to their current age. Children should realise that they will stop growing eventually.

QUESTIONS

○ What happens to your weight and height as you age?

Possible answers

It increases rapidly at first and then slows down and remains almost constant.

Watch out for!

Be aware of children that may be sensitive to being the smallest or largest.

ısk Sheet 6

ne .... Date ....

ısk Sheet 6

ıne ....   *Date* ....

Keeping the life cycle going

Purpose

For children to understand that we have a life cycle and that it includes birth, growth, reproduction and death.

What to do

The **Pupil's Book** shows a pictorial representation of the human life cycle. The stages should be discussed with the class. Children should then try to reflect on their own life cycle and represent it using text and drawings.

A range of questions is included in the **Pupil's Book**, to which the children can respond and show their understanding of the life cycle process.

ICT OPPORTUNITY

Children could word process their documents and include diagrams.

Watch out for!

The emphasis should be on care and love. Sensitivity should be deployed, especially where you are aware of one-parent families and children from broken marriages/partnerships. The school's moral, health and sex education frameworks and policies should be considered and respected.

Family trees

Purpose

For children to apply the concept that humans have a life cycle that includes birth, growth, reproduction and death by introducing family trees. For them to become aware that families can become 'extinct' if children do not grow up and reproduce.

What to do

The **Pupil's Book** shows a way of representing the human life cycle stages in a family tree. Males and females often marry and have children. How 'marriages' and children of marriages are represented on a family tree should be explained to the children. Their understanding of the idea can be assessed by the questions in the **Pupil's Book**. As a longer-term piece of research, children could find out about their own family trees and represent them diagrammatically, perhaps using some photographs as illustrations.

The Extra Challenge provides an opportunity for children to use secondary data to illustrate that mammals have gestation times that vary and this variation is linked to the size of the mammalian species. The table of some mammalian gestation times is given in days. Children could copy this and convert the time periods into weeks by dividing by 7.

Animal	Gestation in days	Gestation in weeks
Mouse	21	3
Rabbit	30	4·3
Lion	108	15·4
Human	252	36
Cow	284	40·6
Horse	336	48
Elephant	624	89·1

QUESTIONS

Possible answers

○ Which of these mammals has the shortest gestation time?

Mouse.

○ Which of these mammals has the longest gestation time?

Elephant.

○ How long is the gestation time of a human?

36 weeks/252 days/nine months.

○ How many mammals in the table have gestation times longer than that of humans? Which are they?

Three. The cow, horse and elephant.

○ How much longer is the elephant's gestation time than a human's?

53·1 weeks/372 days.

○ How does the length of the gestation time appear to be connected to the size of the mammal?

The longer the gestation time the bigger the size of the mammal, the shorter the gestation time the smaller the mammal.

ICT OPPORTUNITY

Children could use DTP or drawing software to draw family trees.

Watch out for!

Sensitivity is needed if children are known to be adopted or if they are from one-parent families and have never known one of their parents. Inventing an 'imaginary' family for all the children to work on may be more appropriate. Take care with the term 'gestation period' – it may be more appropriate to refer to 'gestation time', especially for girls, to avoid any confusion of the term 'period' with 'menstrual period'. Work within the school's agreed sex education policy.

Life spans

TASK 18

Purpose

For children to develop an ability to order results, make bar charts and to seek patterns in a variety of animal life spans.

What to do

The **Pupil's Book** has a table of information about the life span of different animals. It is not in the correct order and the first task is for the children to copy the table and order the data. The number of animals each group considers could be reduced for less able children. The ordered data should be drawn up as a bar chart.

QUESTIONS

Possible answers

○ Which animal has the longest life span?

Human.

○ Which animal has the shortest life span?

House mouse.

○ How much longer than a house mouse is a vampire bat likely to live ?

10 years.

○ How much longer than a herring gull is an eagle owl likely to live ?

27 years.

ICT OPPORTUNITY

Children could use spreadsheets and graphing software to record and present their data.

Survival Game

Purpose

For children to apply the concept that humans have a life cycle and that, in order for the family or indeed the human species to survive, individuals must reproduce.

What to do

In this board game, children travel in a boat through an imaginary planet. They experience good times and disasters. The former are celebrated by the birth of children and the latter by loss of adults and/or children. The game should reinforce the notion that to reproduce there has to be a male and a female. Failure of that group to reproduce can cause a 'family group' to die out. The instructions for the game are in the **Pupil's Book** and the board itself is on **Task Sheet 9**.

Endangered species

Brainstorm a list of endangered species. Encourage the children to choose one and research how it could be protected to prevent it becoming extinct.

ICT OPPORTUNITY

Children could use DTP or a word processor to produce leaflets or posters and use CD-ROMs and the Internet for research.

Summary

An opportunity for the children to assess their own progress using the **Science Log**. Tell the children to circle the face that best reflects how confident they are with each statement.

Assessment Tasks

A

An assessment of children's learning. Give the children **Assessment Task Sheets A** and **B**.
The questions are below, with selected answers in *italics*.

ANSWERS

1 The diagram shows the life cycle of a flowering plant. Write the labels in the correct order, starting with an adult plant.

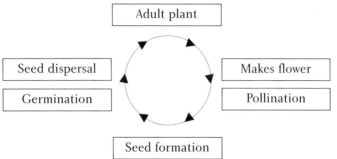

2 a) Look at the diagrams of pollen grains. One of the pollen grains is carried by insects and the other by wind. Which grain is carried by insects? How do you know?
A – *Because it is rough and has spines for sticking to an insect's body.*

b) Why are many flowers brightly coloured and sweetly scented? *To attract insects for pollination.*

B

1 Which special cells are needed to make a new animal? Underline two from the list.

bone cells   <u>sperm cells</u>   muscle cells   <u>egg cells</u>   skin cells

2 Look at the diagram of the flower. Draw lines from the lables to the correct parts.

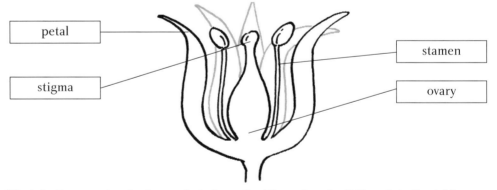

3 What do these parts of a flower do to keep the life cycle going? Complete the table.

Flower part	What it does
Petal	*Attracts insects by being coloured and scented.*
Stigma	*Sticky so that pollen sticks to it.*
Ovary	*The place where the fruit and seed forms after the egg or ovule has been fertilised by the male cell.*
Stamen	*Male part of a flower that makes pollen. The male cell in pollen fertilises the egg which develops into a seed.*

Task Sheet 1

Name .... *Date* ....

Where do you think seeds come from? Draw and write to show your ideas.

Use these words to make a concept map of your ideas about seeds and fruits.

fruit	leaf	plant	flower	seed	pollen

Draw a sequence of pictures to show that plants produce fruits and seeds from their flowers, and that these grow into new plants.

Task Sheet 2

Name .... *Date* ....

Catching on to passing animals

Being blown by the wind

Exploding from a pod

Being eaten by birds or other animals

Task Sheet 3

....

Name .... *Date* ....

Our question:

_____

_____

Our prediction:

_____

_____

We will change:

_____

_____

We will count:

the number of days it takes for germination to occur.

_____

We will keep these things the same to make the test fair:

_____

_____

	Number of days for germination to occur

Task Sheet 4

Name .... *Date* ....

Draw pictures of two different flowers. Write these labels by the correct parts of each flower.

petal	sepal	stamen	style	filament	carpel/pistil

stigma	ovary	anther

Task Sheet 5

Name .... Date ....

Name of plant ....

Stamens and carpel (or pistil)		Petals and sepals	
Number of stamens		Colour of petals	
Length of stamen		Number of petals	
Colour of pollen		Length of petals	
Number of carpels		Colour of sepals	
Length of carpel		Number of sepals	
Colour of stigma		Length of sepals	
Colour of style			
Colour of ovary			

Task Sheet 6

Name .... *Date* ....

New Star Science Ginn and Company 2001
Copying permitted for purchasing school only. This material is not copyright free.

Task Sheet 7

Name .... Date ....

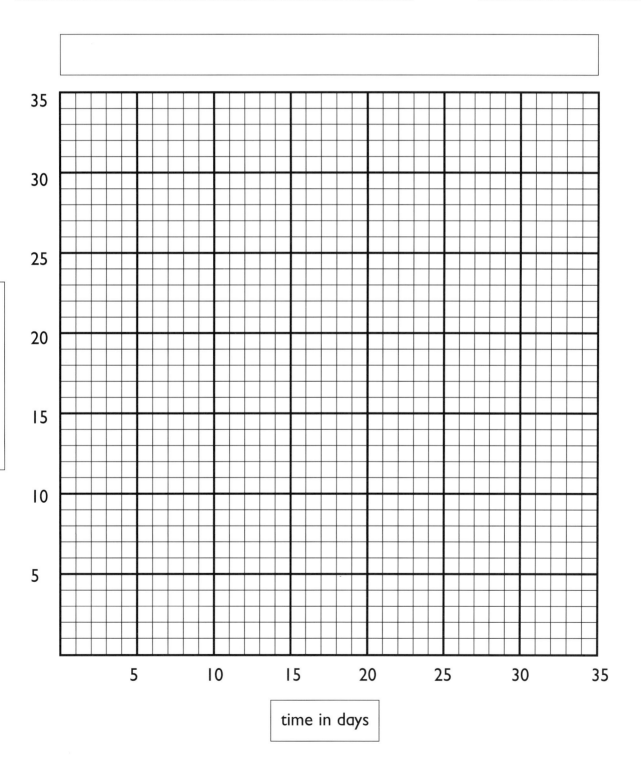

height of plant in cm

time in days

Task Sheet 8

Name .... Date ....

Task Sheet 9

Name .... Date ....

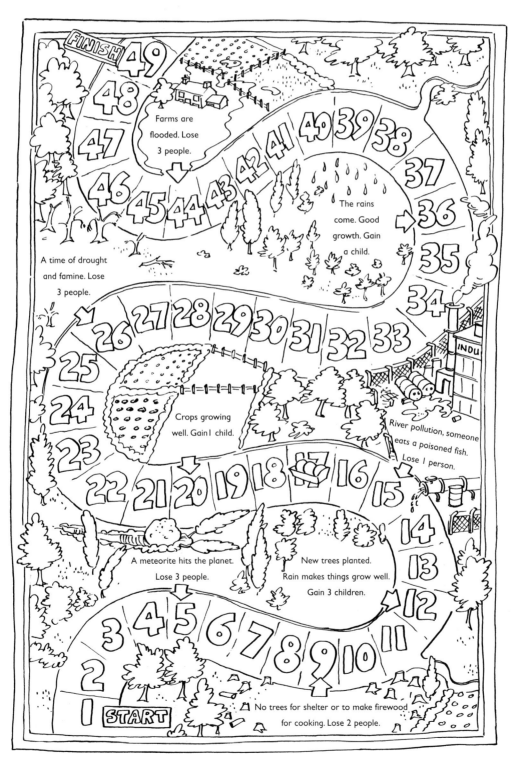

Science Log

Name .... Date ....

- I know that flowering plants reproduce.   😊 😐 ☹️

- I know that seeds provide food for humans and other animals.   😊 😐 ☹️

- I know that seeds are dispersed in different ways.   😊 😐 ☹️

- I know that plants reproduce.   😊 😐 ☹️

- I know that seeds need the right conditions to germinate.   😊 😐 ☹️

- I can plan and carry out a fair test.   😊 😐 ☹️

- I know that plants produce flowers, fruits and seeds.   😊 😐 ☹️

- I know that flowers need pollinating to make fruits and seeds.   😊 😐 ☹️

- I know that insects pollinate some flowers.   😊 😐 ☹️

- I know that animals have a life cycle of birth, growth, reproduction and death.   😊 😐 ☹️

- I know that if living things don't reproduce they die out.   😊 😐 ☹️

Assessment Task Sheet A

Name .... *Date* ....

1 The diagram shows the life cycle of a flowering plant. Write the labels in the correct order, starting with an adult plant.

Adult plant	Seed dispersal	Pollination	Germination	Seed formation	Makes flower

Adult plant

2 a) Look at the diagrams of pollen grains.
One of the pollen grains is carried by insects and the other by wind.
Which grain is carried by insects?
How do you know?

A   B

_____

_____

b) Why are many flowers brightly coloured and sweetly scented?

_____

Assessment Task Sheet B

Name .... Date ....

1 Which special cells are needed to make a new animal? Underline two from the list.

bone cells   sperm cells   muscle cells   egg cells   skin cells

2 Look at the diagram of the flower. Draw lines from the labels to the correct parts.

| petal |

| stamen |

| stigma |

| ovary |

3 What do these parts of a flower do to keep the life cycle going? Complete the table.

Flower part	What it does
Petal	
Stigma	
Ovary	
Stamen	

New Star Science Ginn and Company 2001
Copying permitted for purchasing school only. This material is not copyright free.

Curriculum Links

England National Curriculum

Sc1   Scientific enquiry – *all*

Sc2   Life processes and living things:

Life Processes – 1a, 1b, 1c

Humans and other animals – 2f

Green plants - 3d

Northern Ireland Curriculum

Key Stage 2

Investigating and Making in Science and Technology – *all*

Living Things:

Ourselves – a

Animals and Plants – a, b, h

Environmental Studies 5-14 in Scottish schools

Living Things and the Processes of Life:

Variety and Characteristic Features – level D

The Processes of Life – levels A, B, C, D

Interaction of Living Things with their Environment – level C

Skills in Science: Investigating – *all*

Wales National Curriculum

Key Stage 2

Scientific Enquiry – *all*

Life Processes and Living Things:

Life Processes – 1, 2

Humans and Other Animals – 9

Green Plants as Organisms – 4, 5, 6

NEW STAR SCIENCE SKILLS LADDER

	Planning					Obtaining and presenting evidence			Considering evidence and evaluating			
	Asking questions and having ideas	Deciding an appropriate approach	Planning the detail of what to do	Predicting what might happen	Choosing what equipment to use	Using equipment and carrying out practical work safely	Making observations and taking measurements	Presenting evidence	Drawing conclusions and describing patterns and trends	Comparing results to predictions and making further predictions	Explaining evidence	Evaluating
Year 4	Asks questions and offers own ideas for scientific enquiry.	With support knows when to answer a question by using a fair test and when evidence should be collected in other ways.	In a fair test, identifies what to keep the same and with support what to change and what to measure/observe. Plans main steps in other enquiries. Recognises hazards and, with support, plans how to control risks.	Predicts outcomes and sometimes suggests reasons for their prediction.	Selects appropriate equipment and with support, considers the scale and the degree of accuracy required on some measuring equipment.	Uses basic equipment correctly and safely. Begins to deal with equipment failures.	Makes a series of observations. Uses standard measuring equipment for measuring most quantities.	Creates own tables and bar charts. Uses a line chart with support.	Makes a general statement about simple patterns in results.	Makes further predictions from results in simple contexts.	Provides explanations for simple patterns in results.	Suggests how the enquiry might be improved. With support, recognises some of the limitations of their evidence.
Year 5	Asks questions and offers own ideas for scientific enquiry and, with support, improves question to clarify scientific purpose.	Knows when to answer a question by using a fair test and when evidence should be collected in other ways, including using secondary sources.	Sets up a fair test knowing what to change, what to measure/observe and what to keep the same. With support, considers whether to take repeat readings. With support, plans the detail in other types of enquiry. Assesses hazards and plans how to control risks.	Predicts outcomes and, where appropriate, suggests reasons for their predictions.	Selects equipment from a wider range, including digital scales, forcemeters and computer sensors. With support, considers the scale and the degree of accuracy required on measuring equipment.	Uses a wide range of equipment correctly and safely. Deals with most equipment failures independently.	Makes a series of relevant observations. With support, takes accurate readings on measuring equipment, repeating them where necessary.	Begins to select appropriate way to present evidence. Creates own bar charts and tables, including those for repeat readings. Creates a line graph with support.	With support, describes relationships identified, linking both factors and describing whole relationship in comparative terms.	With support, makes further predictions from results and uses these to test out the suggested pattern in the relationship studied.	Sometimes relates patterns in results to scientific knowledge where appropriate.	Identifies how much to trust results. Suggests reasons why similar enquiries yield different results. With support, considers the spread of repeated measurements. With support, recognises some of the limitations of their evidence.
Year 6	Asks questions and offers own ideas for scientific enquiry which have a clear scientific purpose.	Identifies appropriate approach to answer a scientific question.	Sets up a fair test. Plans the detail in other types of enquiry. Decides whether to take repeat readings. With support, considers whether plans will yield enough evidence for the task. Assesses hazards and plans	Predicts outcomes and, where appropriate, sketches a graph to show the expected pattern in results. Justifies their predictions using scientific knowledge when possible.	Selects suitable equipment for a range of tasks. Takes into account the scale and the degree of accuracy required on measuring equipment.	Uses a wide range of equipment correctly and safely. Deals with equipment failures independently.	Makes a series of relevant observations. Takes accurate readings on measuring equipment, repeating them where necessary.	Selects suitable way to present evidence. Where appropriate, draws up line graph independently, except where scales involve very large or very small numbers.	Describes relationships identified, linking both factors and describing whole relationship in comparative terms.	Makes further predictions from results and uses these to test out the suggested pattern in the relationship studied.	Relates patterns in results to scientific knowledge where appropriate.	Identifies how much to trust results and justifies decision. Suggests reasons why similar enquiries yield different results. Considers the spread of repeated measurements. Recognises some of the limitations of their...